Heracles
and the
Terrible Tasks

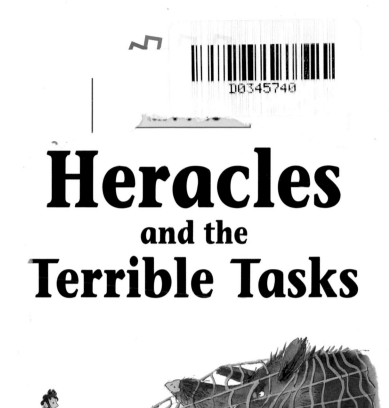

by Peter Cottrill

W
FRANKLIN WATTS

First published in 2009 by
Franklin Watts
338 Euston Road
London
NW1 3BH

Franklin Watts Australia
Level 17/207 Kent Street
Sydney
NSW 2000

A CIP catalogue record for this book is available
from the British Library.

ISBN 978 0 7496 8588 1 (hbk)
ISBN 978 0 7496 8592 8 (pbk)

Series Editor: Melanie Palmer
Series Advisor: Dr Barrie Wade
Series Designer: Peter Scoulding

Printed in China

Franklin Watts is a division of
Hachette Children's Books,
an Hachette UK company
www.hachettelivre.co.uk

Long ago, there lived a
great hero named Heracles.
He was very big and very strong.

But the gods sent him as a slave to serve King Eurystheus and do whatever the King ordered.

"If you want to be free you must go to Nemea and bring me the skin of the man-eating lion," said the King.

As Heracles arrived in Nemea,
the lion leapt straight out at him.

Heracles was not afraid. He wrestled the lion to the ground with his bare hands.

The King couldn't believe his eyes when Heracles returned with the lion's skin. So he thought of another task:

8

"Kill the nine-headed Hydra. Each time you cut off a head, two will grow back," laughed the King. He was sure Heracles would fail.

But Heracles was cunning. He took his cousin, Iolus, to help him.

As he cut off the Hydra's hissing heads, Iolus used a fire torch to stop the heads growing back.

When Heracles returned to the
palace, the King was amazed.
He knew he had to think up lots
of tasks to keep Heracles busy,
so he wrote a long list.

"Capture the golden stag,

and a big, wild boar."

"Clean the stables for
King Aegeus,

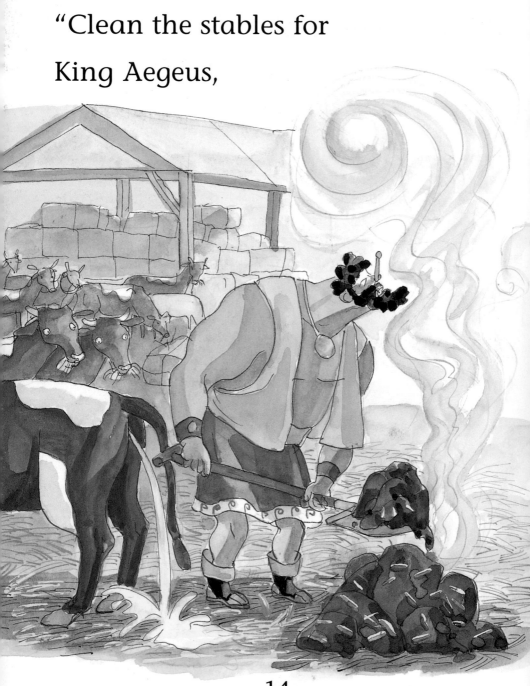

kill some very vicious birds,

and capture the Cretan bull."

"Steal: a herd of horses,

the Amazon Queen's belt,

and cattle from Geryon the giant."

"Phew!" said Hercales. He had now finished ten tasks, but the next was more tricky: "Take sixteen golden apples from the garden of Zeus."

"Hmm, this will offend Zeus, King of the gods," Heracles said, "and that *does* scare me!"

Then Heracles had an idea.

"I'll ask Atlas, the giant who holds up the world, to help me," he thought.

"Atlas, you look tired, why don't you take a break? I'll hold up the world for a while, if you can steal sixteen of Zeus's golden apples," Heracles said.

Atlas needed a rest, so he agreed. Heracles was strong enough to take his place – but only just!

He was very glad to give the world back to Atlas. He grabbed the apples and ran away.

Now there was just one task left:
"Bring me Cerberus, the beast that
guards the Underworld."

No man had ever gone there
and come back alive!

Cerberus snarled and snapped at Heracles with its three heads. It swished its scaly serpent's tail and scratched him with its lion's claws.

But Heracles was clever and quick.

He laid a trap to catch the beast!

Then he returned with a new pet for King Eurystheus.

The King was stunned. He had run out of tasks, so he set Heracles free.

Puzzle 1

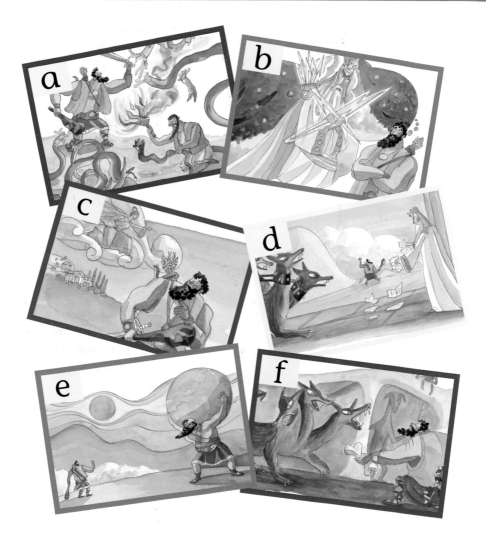

Put these pictures in the correct order.

Which event do you think is most important?

Now retell the story in your own words.

Puzzle 2

Choose the correct speech bubbles for each character. Can you think of any others? Turn over to find the answers.

Answers

Puzzle 1

The correct order is

1c, 2a, 3b, 4e, 5f, 6d

Puzzle 2

Heracles: 1, 6

King Eurystheus: 2, 3

Atlas: 4, 5

Look out for more Hopscotch:

Icarus, the Boy Who Flew
ISBN 978 0 7496 7992 7*
ISBN 978 0 7496 8000 8

**Perseus and the
Snake Monster**
ISBN 978 0 7496 7993 4*
ISBN 978 0 7496 8001 5

**Odysseus and the
Wooden Horse**
ISBN 978 0 7496 7994 1*
ISBN 978 0 7496 8002 2

**Persephone and the
Pomegranate Seeds**
ISBN 978 0 7496 7995 8*
ISBN 978 0 7496 8003 9

Romulus and Remus
ISBN 978 0 7496 7996 5*
ISBN 978 0 7496 8004 6

Thor's Hammer
ISBN 978 0 7496 7997 2*
ISBN 978 0 7496 8005 3

Gelert the Brave
ISBN 978 0 7496 7999 6*
ISBN 978 0 7496 8007 7

No Dinner for Anansi
ISBN 978 0 7496 8006 0

King Midas's Golden Touch
ISBN 978 0 7496 8585 0*
ISBN 978 0 7496 8589 8

**Theseus and the
Minotaur**
ISBN 978 0 7496 8586 7*
ISBN 978 0 7496 8590 4

**Jason's Quest for the
Golden Fleece**
ISBN 978 0 7496 8587 4*
ISBN 978 0 7496 8591 1

**Heracles and the
Terrible Tasks**
ISBN 978 0 7496 8588 1*
ISBN 978 0 7496 8592 8

For more Hopscotch books go to: www.franklinwatts.co.uk

* hardback